DELTA
YOUNG LEARNERS ENGLISH

Mighty Movers
An activity-based course for young learners

Activity Book

Viv Lambert and Wendy Superfine

Mighty Movers

DELTA Publishing
Quince Cottage
Hoe Lane
Peaslake
Surrey GU5 9SW
United Kingdom

Email: mightymovers@deltapublishing.co.uk
www.deltapublishing.co.uk

First published 2007
Reprinted 2011, 2012, 2013

Project managed by Chris Hartley
Edited by Karen Gray
Designed by Peter Bushell
Illustrations by Claire Mumford, Geo Parkin and Peter Stevenson
Photographs by Michael Little Photography, with thanks to Reigate Priory School
Printed in China by RR Donnelley

ISBN: 978 1 905085 06 4

Contents

1 **Read and write**

pirate having
ten wearing
dragon clown

It's Peter's birthday. He's **1** _having_ a birthday party. He's **2** .... years old now. Jim's a **3** .... and Uncle Fred's a **4** .... He's **5** .... a long green coat. Sally's a **6** .... with curly orange hair!

2 **Look at the pictures and write the names**

1

.... Sally ....

2

....

3

....

4

....

3 **Listen and write the words** 1

1 How old's Peter? .... _ten_ ....

2 What's the name of Peter's cousin? ....

3 What's the name of Peter's uncle? ....

4 What colour's Uncle Fred's hat? ....

5 What colour's Sally's hair? ....

LESSON 2

1 Read, draw and colour

Colour Uncle Fred's hat black and his coat green.

Colour Sally's hair purple.

Draw a flower on Peter's aunt's sweater.

Colour the dragon green.

Draw a banana in Paul's hand.

2 Look at the picture and write *yes* or *no*

1 Jim's a tall pirate. ......no......

2 The pirate's wearing a long coat. ....

3 Sally's hair is red. ....

4 Paul's got curly purple hair. ....

5 Peter's aunt is wearing a sweater. ....

3 Read and write

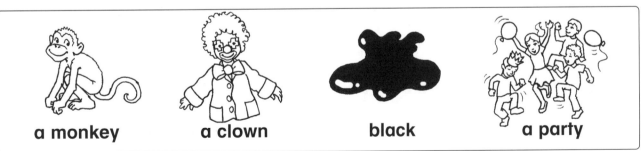

a monkey **a clown** **black** **a party**

1 You have this when it is your birthday. ....party.............

2 This animal is brown and has a long tail. ....

3 A pirate's hat is usually this colour. ....

4 He's funny and has got orange curly hair. ....

1 **Look at the picture in the Pupil's Book and complete the sentences**

1 The pirate is Peter's ……uncle…………………… .

2 He's wearing a black ……………………………… .

3 The monkey's eating a ……………………………… .

4 The clown's got curly orange ……………………………… .

5 The dragon's talking to Peter's ……………………………… .

2 **Listen and draw lines** 🎧 2

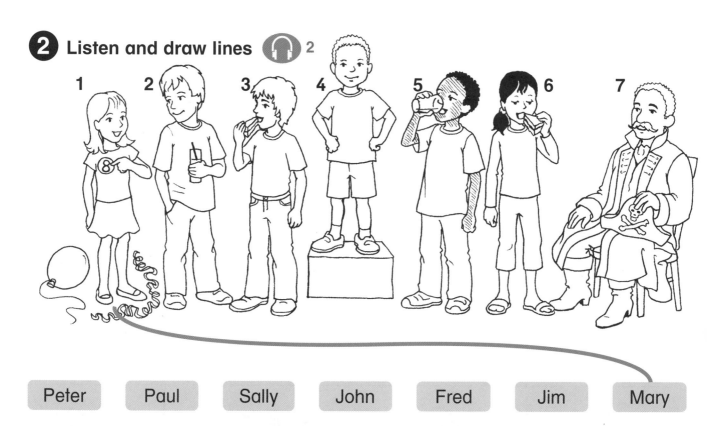

| Peter | Paul | Sally | John | Fred | Jim | Mary |

3 **Read and choose the best answer**

1 What's Uncle Fred wearing?   **a** a tall hat   **b** a long coat

2 What's Paul eating?   **a** some juice   **b** a sandwich

3 Has Sally got fair hair?   **a** No, she hasn't.   **b** Yes, it is.

4 Who's Peter's sister?   **a** She's got Mary.   **b** She's called Mary.

5 Is Jim standing on a box?   **a** No, there isn't.   **b** Yes, he is.

LESSON 4

1 Listen and tick the box 3

1 What's the clown wearing?

2 What's the pirate got?

3 What's the dragon eating?

2 Read and write the words

curly   long
green   tall
eating

There are a lot of children at Peter's party. Sally's a clown with **1** _curly_ orange hair. The pirate is very **2** _____ and is wearing a **3** _____ coat. He's got a parrot which is red and **4** _____ . Jim's a dragon. He's very hungry and is **5** _____ birthday cake!

3 Find and write the words

elephant ....

f	c	t	l	w	b	a	c	i
e	l	e	p	h	a	n	t	i
l	o	e	a	i	l	m	s	c
t	w	a	r	o	r	q	f	e
u	n	l	r	e	o	a	x	c
w	l	f	o	c	p	u	t	r
b	m	o	t	y	c	k	s	e
y	p	k	a	p	e	e	d	a
b	a	l	l	o	o	n	d	m

....

1 **Look at picture A in the Pupil's Book and write** *yes* **or** *no*

1 Paul's wearing a football shirt. ....no.....

2 John's playing badminton. ....

3 Sally's wearing an orange T-shirt and shorts. ....

4 Peter's wearing a blue and white football shirt. ....

5 Mary's wearing a blue skirt. ....

2 **Look at pictures A and B. Write about the differences.**

1 What's Mary wearing in picture A? .....*a blue skirt*.....

2 What's she wearing in picture B? ....

3 What's John doing in picture A? ....

4 What's he doing in picture B? ....

5 What's Peter holding in picture A? ....

6 What's he holding in picture B? ....

3 **Look at the pictures and the letters. Write the words.**

1   <u>football</u>   4   _ _ _ _ _ _ _ _

2  _ _ _ _ _   5  _ _ _ _ _ _ _

3  _ _ _ _   6   _ _ _

LESSON 6

1 **Read the story and write the words**

My name's Ann. I like reading books and listening to ⬤ **1** ....CDs....... .

I love stories about animals and about people. I'm reading a story about a

pirate who lives on an 🌴 **2** .... with his parrot. The pirate eats

🐟 **3** .... and 🍇 **4** .... and vegetables that grow

there. In this story a boy swims to the 🌴 **5** .... and he sees

the 🏴‍☠️ **6** .... The pirate says, 'Hello, What's your name?' The

boy says, 'Hello, I'm Jim. What's your name ?' The pirate's name is Pip. The

next day Jim sees a big green bird flying behind a tree. At first he's afraid, then

the bird says, 'Where's Pip? Where's Pip?' The boy laughs and says, 'Come

with me' and he takes the bird back to Pip. Pip's very pleased to see his

🦜 **7** .... ! I like the story a lot!

2 **Choose the correct words and write them on the lines**

1   I _like_ reading books.   **like   likes   liked**

2   The pirate .... fish and fruit and vegetables.   **eat   eating   eats**

3   The boy .... , 'Hello, I'm Jim.'   **say   says   saying**

4   Jim .... a big green bird.   **sees   see   sea**

5   He .... the bird back to Pip.   **take   talking   takes**

3 **Draw a book cover and write the title**

1 Circle the odd one out and tell a friend

Sally isn't a boy.

1

2

4

3

5

2 Read and write

1 Pip the pirate lives on an __island__ .

2 A _____ is brown and lives in the jungle.

3 You wear a _____ over your clothes.

4 Your _____ is your dad's sister.

5 A _____ wears funny clothes.

Crossword:
1 i
s
l
3
4 a
5
n
d
2

3 Write the answers for you. Then ask a friend.

1 Have you got an aunt or an uncle? _____

2 What are they called? _____

3 What colour's your hair? _____

4 Are you tall or short? _____

5 What are you wearing? _____

1 Read and write *yes* or *no*

1 Has Pip the pirate got a long nose? .....yes.....

2 Is the parrot called Pat? ....

3 Has the clown got straight hair? ....

4 Has the elephant got a short nose? ....

5 Is the elephant strong? ....

6 Is the clown called Coco? ....

Look at the song in the Pupil's Book.

2 Make a party invitation. Tell a friend. ➡ Cut-out 1

To Jane. Please come to my party at 3 o'clock on Sunday at Megabowl. From Sarah.

Invitation

Well done!

3 Tick what you can do. Colour the ladder.

I can say family words. ☐

I can write the names of party characters. ☐

I can describe my family. ☐

I can write about what I'm wearing. ☐

I can read a story. ☐

Very good

Good

OK

11

1 Read and write

swim   treasure
map   must
beach   lake

Peter and Mary are on the **1** ____beach____ . They find a box with **2** _____ in it. Peter looks at a **3** _____ . They see a **4** _____ which is near their house. They mustn't **5** _____ in the lake. When they see a rainbow, they **6** _____ go to the big tree.

2 Look at the pictures and write the words

1

2

3

4

_____ box _____   _____   _____   _____

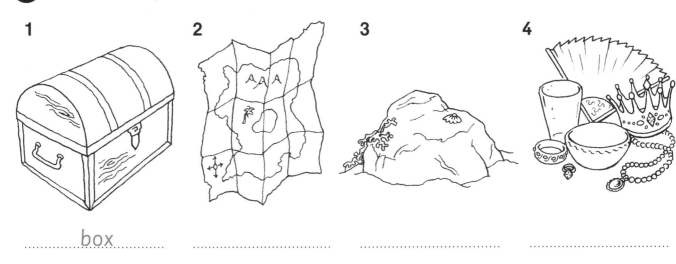

3 Listen and write the words 4

1   Mary, you must be ____careful____ !

2   Look, this is a map of an _____ .

3   That's the lake which is _____ our house.

4   You _____ swim in the lake.

5   When you see a _____ , you must go to the big tree.

 12

LESSON 2

UNIT **2**

1 Read, draw and colour

Colour the box black and brown.

Colour the bowl red and the blanket green.

Draw a house on the map.

Colour the fan purple, blue and orange.

Draw a yellow cup in the box.

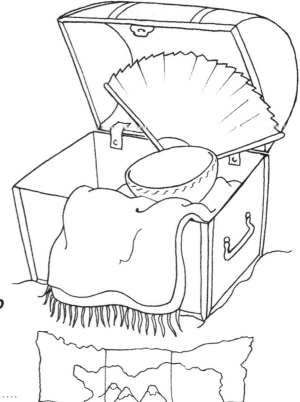

2 Look at the picture and write *yes* or *no*

1   There's a glass in the box. ....no....

2   The fan's purple, blue and orange. ....

3   The blanket is brown. ....

4   The cup in the box is yellow. ....

5   There's a house on the map. ....

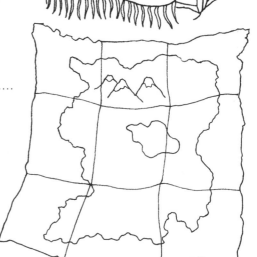

3 Read and write

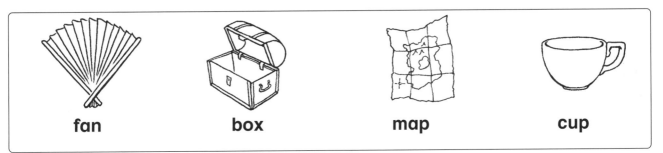

| **fan** | **box** | **map** | **cup** |

1   You can drink tea out of this. ....cup........

2   You put things in this. ....

3   You use this when you are hot. ....

4   You use this to show you the way. ....

UNIT **2**

LESSON **3**

1 **Look at the picture in the Pupil's Book and complete the sentences**

1 The .... *rainbow* .... is behind Peter and Sally.

2 They are sitting on a ....

3 The map is in front of the .... of fruit.

4 The .... is next to the bowl.

5 The .... is very old.

2 **Listen and draw lines** 🎧 5

| Tuesday | Wednesday | Thursday | Friday | Saturday |

3 **Read and choose the best answer**

1 Can you swim in the sea? **a** Yes, I do. **b** (Yes, I can.)

2 Must you be careful? **a** Yes, I must. **b** Yes, I mustn't.

3 Does the map look dirty? **a** Yes, it does. **b** No, it isn't.

4 Where are you in this photo? **a** in the beach **b** at the beach

5 Have you got a camera? **a** Yes, I must. **b** No, I haven't.

1 Listen and tick the box 6

1 What's Sue doing?

 A

 B ✔

 C

2 What are they eating?

 A

 B

 C

3 What's Sue looking at?

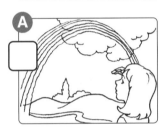 A

 B

 C

2 Read and write the words

Sue's having an exciting ❶ _holiday_ . She's going

to the beach ❷ .... day and eating

❸ .... for lunch. She's taking photos of

everything with her new ❹ .... She wants to

find ❺ .... treasure!

> **sandwiches**
> **every camera**
> ~~holiday~~ **some**

3 Find and write the words

rainbow

....

....

....

....

....

r	u	p	s	l	e	c	r
i	a	l	c	a	b	h	i
o	s	i	c	a	f	e	w
w	s	l	n	u	r	e	o
e	t	h	a	b	m	s	l
y	f	b	k	n	o	e	a
u	l	p	e	n	d	w	k
t	r	e	a	s	u	r	e

UNIT 2   **LESSON 5**

1   **Look at picture A in the Pupil's Book and write *yes* or *no***

1   There are four mountains at the top of the island. ___no___

2   There's a monkey in the lake. ....

3   There's a box under the tree. ....

4   You must swim in the lake. ....

5   There's an old house at the bottom of the island. ....

2   **Look at pictures A and B. Write about the differences.**

1   There are three mountains in A but there's one ___mountain___ in B.

2   There's a crocodile in the lake in A, but there's an .... in B.

3   The box is under the tree in A, but it's next to the .... in B.

4   The house is old in A, but the house is .... in B.

5   There's a monkey in the tree in A, but there isn't a .... in B.

6   You mustn't swim in the lake in A, but you can .... in B.

3   **Look at the pictures and the letters. Write the words.**

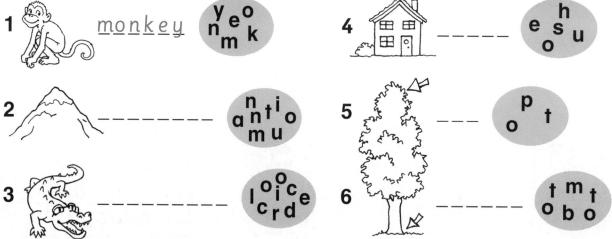

1   _monkey_   y e o n e k m k

2   _ _ _ _ _ _ _ _   n t i a n o m u

3   _ _ _ _ _ _ _ _   o i c l c r e d

4   _ _ _ _ _   h e s u o

5   _ _ _   p o t

6   _ _ _ _ _ _   t m t o b o

16

1 **Read the story and write the words**

Vicky lives with her  **1** ...parents... and her two brothers, Jack and

Fred, in a **2** .... Jack's ten, Vicky's eight and Fred's five.

This week, they're on holiday by the **3** .... They have

their **4** .... in the garden because it's hot. Fred doesn't want

any. They all go to the **5** .... and the sea is very blue.

There are three beautiful **6** .... in the water! Jack looks at

them. He runs to the sea and swims. Then Jack's dad throws a ball into the

sea and the dolphins play with it. Dad **7** .... a photo with his

camera. It's a great picture!

2 **Choose the correct words and write them on the lines**

1   Vicky ......lives...... with her parents.   **lives   live   love**

2   They have .... breakfast in the garden.   **her   their   there**

3   They all go to the ....   **beech   beach   sea**

4   Jack .... at the dolphins.   **look   looking   looks**

5   Dad .... a ball into the sea.   **throws   through   two**

3 **Draw a book cover and write the title**

17

1 **Circle the odd one out and tell a friend**

A monkey doesn't swim in the sea.

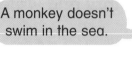

1

2

4

3

5

2 **Read and write**

1 You can eat soup in a ____bowl____ .

2 You put a _____ on your bed.

3 You can drink milk out of a _____ .

4 A _____ swims in the sea.

5 You have a _____ outside.

6 You take photos with a _____ .

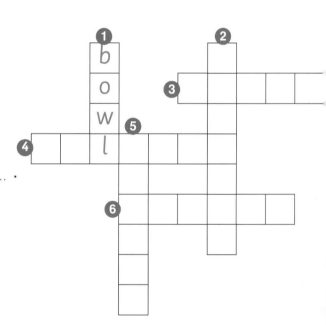

3 **Write the answers for you. Then ask a friend.**

1 Where do you go on holiday? _____

2 Who do you go with? _____

3 What do you do on holiday? _____

4 What do you take on holiday? _____

5 How do you get there? _____

❶ Read and write *yes* or *no*

1 You must never smile at a crocodile. ....yes....

2 The crocodile lives in the river. ....

3 He's awake. ....

4 You must talk to the crocodile. ....

5 You must run away. ....

6 You must say 'Good morning!' ....

Look at the song in the Pupil's Book.

❷ Make a map. Tell a friend. ➡ Cut-out 2

Go to the top of the map. Look next to the mountain under the big tree.

Well done!

❸ Tick what you can do. Colour the ladder.

I can say the names of things on an island. ☐

I can say what I must/mustn't do. ☐

I can spell holiday words. ☐

I can write about my holidays. ☐

I can describe a map. ☐

Very good

Good

OK

19

UNIT 3 My body

1 Read and write

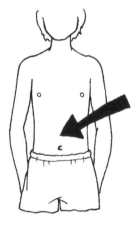

temperature
doctor   wrong
fine   lunch
hurts

Paul's got backache. His dad takes him to the

1 ......_doctor_...... . The doctor says there is nothing

2 .... with his back. Paul's got a headache.

The doctor takes his 3 .... It is

4 .... Now Paul's leg 5 ....

His 6 .... is in his sock!

2 Look at the pictures and write the names

1   2   3   4

......_stomach_...... ....

3 Listen and write the words 🎧 7

1 What's the ....._matter_..... ?

2 You .... go to the doctor.

3 My back hurts ....

4 There's .... wrong with your back.

5 Now my .... hurts.

20

LESSON 2

1 Read, draw and colour

Colour Peter's T-shirt green.

Colour Dad's trousers brown and his shirt yellow.

Draw a picture of a tree on the wall.

Colour the doctor's moustache and beard black.

Draw a cross on the nurse's dress and colour it red.

2 Look at the picture and write *yes* or *no*

1   Dad and Paul are at the sports centre. ....no....

2   Peter has got a stomach-ache. ....

3   The doctor's taking Paul's temperature. ....

4   The doctor's got a black moustache. ....

5   There's a picture of a tree on the wall. ....

3 Read and write

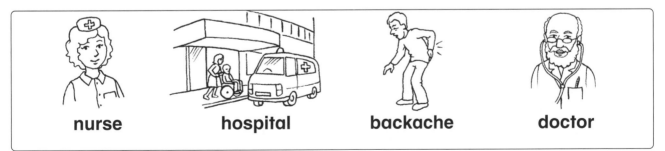

| nurse | hospital | backache | doctor |

1   He helps people who aren't well. ....doctor........

2   You go to this place when you aren't well. ....

3   She works in a hospital and takes your temperature. ....

4   You have this if your back hurts. ....

UNIT **3**

LESSON **3**

1 **Look at the picture in the Pupil's Book and complete the sentences**

1 Paul's ....*carrying*........... a fishing rod.

2 Peter's .... a book about football.

3 Dad's .... the piano.

4 Mum's .... a cookery book.

5 Sally's .... a video.

2 **Listen and draw lines** 🎧 8

1   2   3   4

| Jack | | Jane | | Tom | | Jill |

3 **Read and choose the best answer**

1 Does Paul like going fishing?   **a** Yes, he does.   **b** No, he can't.

2 Does Sally like watching videos?   **a** Yes, she is.   **b** Yes, she does.

3 Do you like reading books about football?   **a** No, I'm not.   **b** No, I don't.

4 Have you got a cold?   **a** No, I haven't.   **b** No, I won't.

5 Does your leg hurt?   **a** Yes, it does.   **b** No, it isn't.

1 Listen and tick the box 9

1 What's the girl doing?

 A

 B ✔

 C

2 What's the boy throwing?

 A

 B

 C

3 What are the children doing?

 A

 B

 C

2 Read and write the words

Sam ❶ ___likes___ doing sport. He likes running and

❷ _____ . He's very good at ❸ _____

and kicking balls. He can ❹ _____ a football

across a field. Today he can't do sport because he's got a

❺ _____ .

| stomach-ache |
| ~~likes~~ jumping |
| throwing kick |

3 Find and write the words

backache

_____

_____

_____

_____

_____

t	f	k	i	b	w	m	p	e
k	o	y	a	q	j	c	t	a
f	n	o	e	w	l	o	h	r
b	c	y	t	s	a	u	g	a
v	c	o	g	h	z	g	x	c
b	v	f	l	p	a	h	j	h
s	h	e	a	d	a	c	h	e
u	m	j	r	s	d	l	h	q
v	b	a	c	k	a	c	h	e

1 **Look at picture A in the Pupil's Book and write *yes* or *no***

1   Daisy's drinking a glass of water.   _yes_

2   Mary's got a stomach-ache.   ....

3   Peter's rowing.   ....

4   Sally's got a headache.   ....

5   Dad's standing by the door.   ....

2 **Look at pictures A and B. Write about the differences.**

1   Daisy isn't drinking water, she's   _got toothache_   .

2   Peter isn't skipping, he's   ....

3   Mary hasn't got stomach-ache, she's   ....

4   Sally isn't cycling, she's   ....

5   Paul isn't rowing, he's   ....

6   Dad isn't standing by the door, ...   is standing by the door.

3 **Look at the pictures and the letters. Write the words.**

1   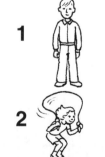 _s t a n d i n g_   a i n s d g t n

4    _ _ _ _ _ _   g r o i n w

2   _ _ _ _ _ _ _   s p n i i k p g

5   _ _ _ _ _ _   r i g n i n d k

3   _ _ _ _ _ _   n c l i g y c

6   _ _ _ _ _ _   i n g n n u r

LESSON 6

1 Read the story and write the words

John isn't well today. He's at home in ![bed] **1** ....*bed*.......... . The doctor

comes to his ![house] **2** .... He says, 'Hello John. How are you?'

John says, 'I'm not very well.' The doctor asks him to open his

![mouth] **3** .... He says, 'Have you got ![face] **4** .... ?'

John says, 'No, I've got a headache and an earache'. Then the doctor takes

his ![thermometer] **5** .... 'I think you have got a bad cold,' says the

doctor. 'You must stay in bed for ![hand] **6** .... days and then you can

go downstairs. What do you like eating?' John says, 'My favourite food is

![ice cream] **7** .... !' The doctor says he can have some ice cream when

he's better!

2 Choose the correct words and write them on the lines

1 John's not ....*well*.......... today. | **will   well   wall** |

2 The doctor asks him to open his .... | **teeth   eyes   mouth** |

3 Then the doctor .... his temperature. | **taking   catches   takes** |

4 I think you've got a bad .... | **cold   hot   foot** |

5 Then John can go .... | **hospital   downstairs   stairs** |

3 Draw a book cover and write the title

1 **Circle the odd one out and tell a friend**

Your back isn't a part of your face.

1

2   4

3   5

2 **Read and write**

1 The doctor has a ...... *beard* ...... on his face.

2 Your .... is between your head and your shoulder.

3 He can .... the ball very far.

4 You go to the .... when you aren't well.

5 Your .... are in your mouth.

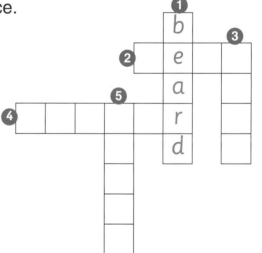

3 **Write the answers for you. Then ask a friend.**

1 Have you got toothache? ....

2 What's your doctor's name? ....

3 Do you know a man with a beard? ....

4 Do you like running or jumping? ....

5 Do you like reading? ....

1 **Read and write *yes* or *no***

1 Your head is at the top of your body. .....yes.....

2 Your neck is between your head and your body. ....

3 Your arm is next to your leg. ....

4 Your stomach is in the middle of your face. ....

5 Your teeth are in your ears. ....

6 Your toes are on your feet. ....

2 **Choose four characters. Ask a friend.** ➡ Cut-out 3

Has your dragon got toothache?

No, it hasn't.

Well done!

3 **Tick what you can do. Colour the ladder.**

I can say the names of some illnesses. ☐

I can say parts of the body. ☐

I can write parts of the body. ☐

I can talk about activities. ☐

I can design a book cover. ☐

Very good

Good

OK

27

UNIT 4 Time to play

LESSON 1

1 Read and write

likes football
name morning
often swimming

My name's Peter. I play **1** _football_ on Saturdays. I play in the **2** _____ .

I also like **3** _____ and I

4 _____ go to the swimming pool.

My friend's **5** _____ is Sally.

She **6** _____ swimming too.

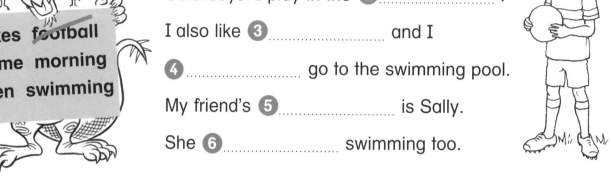

2 Look at the pictures and write the words

1   2   3   4

sports centre   _____   _____   _____

_____   _____   _____   _____

3 Listen and write the words 10

1   Sally wants to go to the swimming pool on _____Saturday_____ .

2   Peter likes going for a swim _____ school.

3   Peter takes the _____ road.

4   Peter goes to the sports _____ .

5   Peter is very hot and _____ .

28

1 Read, draw and colour

Colour Peter's shirt red.

Now colour the clock blue.

Colour Sally's shoes brown and draw a green star on her sweater.

Draw an ice cream in Peter's hand.

Colour Sally's ice cream pink.

2 Look at the picture and write *yes* or *no*

1 Peter's playing football. ....no.....

2 Sally's at the swimming pool. ....

3 Peter's eating an ice cream. ....

4 They're at the shopping centre. ....

5 There's a clock on the wall. ....

3 Read and write

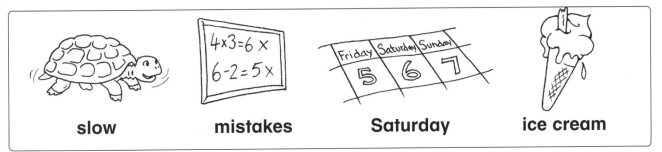

| slow | mistakes | Saturday | ice cream |

1 Peter always plays football on this day. .....Saturday.....

2 Peter says he never makes these. ....

3 Peter is often like this. ....

4 Sally always eats this when she's hot. ....

1 **Look at the picture in the Pupil's Book and complete the sentences**

1 Peter ....*does*.......... his homework on Mondays.

2 He .... hockey on Wednesdays.

3 He goes .... on Tuesdays.

4 He .... skating on Fridays.

5 He plays .... on Thursdays.

2 **Listen and draw lines** 11

1   2   3   4 SPORTS CENTRE   5

Monday   Wednesday   Thursday   Saturday   Sunday

3 **Read and choose the best answer**

1 Peter, can you come swimming this afternoon? **a** Yes, I can **b** No, I don't.

2 Can you come to the cinema? **a** No, I can't. **b** No, I'm not.

3 Is this the swimming pool? **a** No, there isn't. **b** No, it isn't.

4 Do you know the way to the pool? **a** Yes, I do. **b** No, I can't.

5 When can you come? **a** At Friday. **b** On Friday.

LESSON 4

1 Listen and tick the box 12

1 What does Kim do in the morning?

2 What does Kim do in the afternoon?

3 What does Kim do in the evening?

2 Read and write the words

Kim eats **1** _breakfast_ in the morning. Then she **2** .... a bus to school. She goes **3** .... in the afternoon and sometimes she plays a **4** .... with her **5** ....

3 Find and write the words

1  _wash_

2  3

4  5  6

```
g s c h o o l t
t h k o v w h g
b o u m g a m e
z w u e w s o u
i e f w e h v t
x r p o b u s i
b o i r y a d e
l q u k p m v g
```

 31

1 **Look at picture A in the Pupil's Book and write *yes* or *no***

Where's Peter?

1   Peter's on a bus going to school. ......*yes*......

2   Mum's up a tree. ....

3   Mum's inside the cinema. ....

4   Sally's outside the cinema. ....

5   Mary's at the swimming pool. ....

2 **Look at pictures A and B. Write about the differences.**

1   Where's Peter in picture A?   ......*He's on*................ the bus.

2   Where is he in picture B?   .... the cinema.

3   Where's Mum in picture A?   .... the house.

4   Where is she in picture B?   .... the bus.

5   Where's Mary in picture A?   .... the swimming pool.

6   Where is she in picture B?   .... the house.

3 **Look at the pictures and the letters. Write the words.**

1    *c i n e m a*   a n i e m c

4    _ _ _ _ _ _ _ _   r b a t a k f e s

2   _ _ _ _ _   e s u o h

5   _ _ _ _ _   h u l n c

3   _ _ _ _ _ _   b o l f a t l

6   _ _ _ _   r t e e

LESSON **6**

UNIT **4**

1 **Read the story and write the words**

Last Saturday I went to the CINEMA **1** ....cinema.... with my friend Mary.

The **2** .... was called Treasure Island. We sat down in

the third row. 'I can't see very well,' Mary said. There was a tall lady in the

second row in front of us. She had very **3** .... hair. We

watched the first part of the film when Mary said quietly, 'Let's go and buy

an **4** ....' The lady said, 'Be quiet'. It was very dark but we

went outside and bought ice creams. We went back inside and found our

5 .... again. The lady said, 'Shhh!'. Then Mary dropped her

ice cream on the lady's coat. Mary started **6** .... After the

film finished the lights came on. The lady turned around. It was our teacher,

Miss Green. She wasn't very happy when she saw us. We didn't tell her

about the ice cream on her **7** .... !

2 **Choose the correct words and write them on the lines**

1 Last Saturday I ...went.... to the cinema.   **go   goes   went**

2 We .... down in the third row.   **put   sat   sit**

3 There was a tall lady .... front of us.   **in   on   up**

4 It .... very dark.   **were   is   was**

5 The lady was .... teacher.   **your   their   our**

3 **Draw a book cover and write the title**

33

1 **Circle the odd one out and tell a friend**

A sock isn't a part of your body.

1

2

4

3

5

2 **Read and write**

1 You wash in the ___shower___ .

2 Your _____ is next to your arm.

3 A _____ is in the bathroom.

4 An _____ is a very big animal.

5 You eat _____ in the morning.

6 You can watch a _____ on TV.

1
| s |
| h |
| o |
| w |
| e |
| r |

3 **Write the answers for you. Then ask a friend.**

1 How old are you? _____

2 When's your birthday? _____

3 What do you like doing on your birthday? _____

4 What do you like watching on TV? _____

5 What's your favourite film? _____

LESSON 8

1 **Read and write yes or no**

Look at the calendar in the Pupil's Book.

1   Is the eighth a Monday? ....yes....

2   Is the twenty-third a Sunday? ....

3   Is the sixteenth a Tuesday? ....

4   Is the nineteenth a Saturday? ....

5   Is the twenty-second a Friday? ....

6   Is the first a Monday? ....

2 **Make a diary. Tell a friend.** ➡ Cut-out 4

On Sundays, I visit my grandparents.

I go swimming on Saturdays.

Well done!

3 **Tick what you can do. Colour the ladder.**

I can say the days of the week. ☐

I can talk about what I do each day. ☐

I can write about what I do each day. ☐

I can say dates. ☐

I can tell a story. ☐

Very good

Good

OK

5 What's the weather like?

1 Read and write

Tuesday   flew
home   ~~Monday~~
lost   looked

Sally went on holiday last week. **1** ...Monday......

was good. She **2** .... her kite in

the park. It rained on **3** ....

They **4** .... their dog.

They **5** .... for Sammy.

They found him at **6** ....

2 Look at the pictures and write the words

1

2
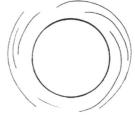

3

4

......rain............   ....

3 Listen and write the words 13

1   Did you have a good ......holiday...... ?

2   What was the .... like?

3   We .... for a long walk with our dog Sammy.

4   We went home and Mum .... the police.

5   We .... so happy!

1 Read, draw and colour

Colour Sally's kite blue and red.

Draw a big cloud in the sky.

Colour the sun yellow.

Colour Sammy brown.

Draw a bowl of biscuits next to Sammy.

2 Look at the picture and write *yes* or *no*

1 Sally's kite is blue and green. ....no....

2 It's raining and snowing. ....

3 Sammy's a brown dog. ....

4 Sammy's lying in the sun. ....

5 The weather's windy and sunny. ....

3 Read and write

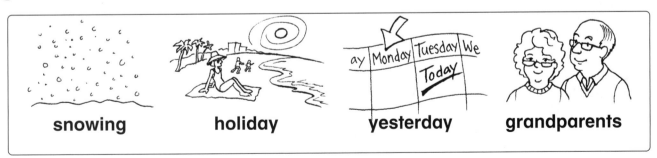

| snowing | holiday | yesterday | grandparents |

1 This is when you are not at school or at work. .....holiday.........

2 These are your mum or dad's parents. ....

3 On Daisy's holiday, the weather was like this on Thursday. ....

4 This is the day before today. ....

1 **Look at the picture in the Pupil's Book and complete the sentences**

1   Yesterday Sally's family ....*went*.......... to the park.

2   Sally .... her kite.

3   Jim .... with his dog.

4   Dad .... a boat.

5   Mum .... round the lake.

2 **Listen and draw lines** 14

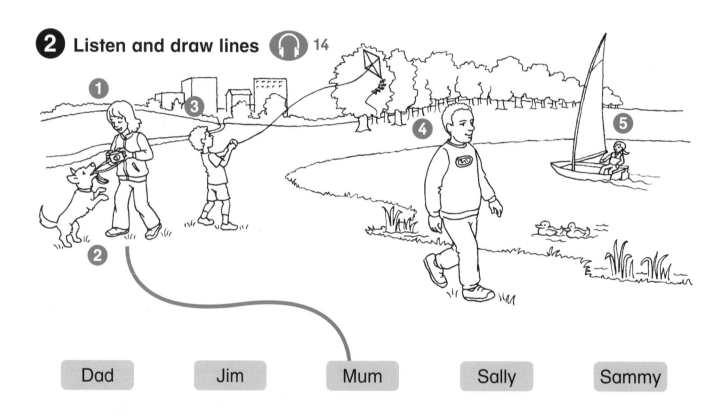

| Dad | Jim | Mum | Sally | Sammy |

3 **Read and choose the best answer**

1   When did Sally fly her kite?   **a** on Monday   **b** at Tuesday

2   Shall I walk round the lake with you?   **a** I can walk there.   **b** Yes, I'd like tha

3   Was the weather sunny on Friday?   **a** No, it isn't.   **b** Yes, it was.

4   Is Jim playing with his dog?   **a** Yes, he is.   **b** No, there isn't.

5   Did Dad sail the boat yesterday?   **a** I've got an idea.   **b** Yes, I think so.

LESSON 4

1 Listen and tick the box 🎧 15

1 What was the weather like?

 A
 B ✔
 C

2 What did Jim buy?

 A
 B
 C

3 What did Jim do yesterday?

 A
 B
 C

2 Read and write the words

hot ~~country~~
puppy
DVD cold

Vicky went to the **1** ...country... at the weekend.

It wasn't **2** .... , it was **3** ....

and it was snowing. She went to the pet shop and

bought a new **4** .... Then she watched

a **5** .... at home.

3 Find and write the words

played

....

....

....

....

....

g	f	p	l	a	y	e	d
n	a	f	d	w	l	i	h
s	b	p	o	d	w	x	u
s	k	o	j	e	a	b	f
a	k	l	u	z	t	q	l
c	t	a	m	g	c	y	e
w	r	n	t	v	h	d	w
m	h	u	t	e	e	t	f
r	a	i	n	e	d	k	v

1 Look at picture A in the Pupil's Book and write *yes* or *no*

I'm hot!

1 Sally's on the beach. ....*yes*....

2 She's wearing a hat. ....

3 Peter and Paul are walking the dog. ....

4 John's at the shops. ....

5 It's sunny and hot. ....

2 Look at pictures A and B. Write about the differences.

1 Today Sally's on the beach but yesterday she ....*was at the shops*.... .

2 Today the weather is sunny but yesterday it ....

3 Today it's hot but yesterday it ....

4 Today John's in the sea but yesterday he ....

5 Today Peter and Paul are on the beach
but yesterday they ....

6 Today it is dry but yesterday it ....

3 Look at the pictures and the letters. Write the words.

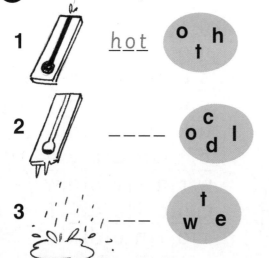

1 <u>h o t</u>   (o h t)

2 _ _ _ _   (c o d l)

3 _ _ _   (t w e)

4 _ _ _ _ _   (d o u l c)

5 _ _ _ _   (o p s h)

6 _ _ _ _ _ _ _ _ _   (s d e e t a y y r)

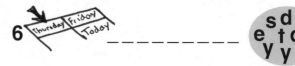

1 **Read the story and write the words**

On Saturday it was 〔sun〕 **1** ....sunny.... and windy, so Paul and his family

went 〔boat〕 **2** .... in their boat. Later, Paul got a bad stomach-ache,

and his dad said they must go to the shops and buy some medicine.

In the 〔city〕 **3** .... , Mum said she wanted to buy some

〔fruit〕 **4** .... Paul said he was feeling better and he wanted to

buy a 〔comic〕 **5** .... His sister said she wanted to buy a new

〔cat〕 **6** .... Then it started to 〔rain〕 **7** .... and they got

wet. When they got home it was dry so Paul read his comic in the garden.

He forgot all about his 〔boy〕 **8** ....

2 **Choose the correct words and write them on the lines**

1   On Saturday it ....was........ sunny and windy.   **is   was   were**

2   Paul .... a bad stomach-ache.   **get   has   got**

3   Paul's dad .... they must go to the shops.   **said   say   wants**

4   Paul .... a new comic.   **forgot   bought   buy**

5   Paul .... his comic in the garden.   **reading   reads   read**

3 **Draw a book cover and write the title**

1 Circle the odd one out and tell a friend.

A cloud isn't an animal.

1

2

4

3

5

2 Read and write

1 ....Snow.... is white and very cold.

2 When it rains there's a lot of ....

3 You can climb up the ....

4 You dry yourself with a ....

5 A .... can fly in the sky.

6 The .... is yellow and very hot.

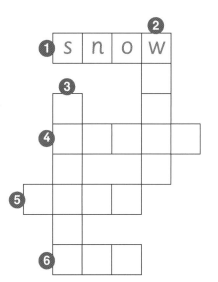

① s | n | o | w ②
③
④
⑤
⑥

3 Write the answers for you. Then ask a friend.

1 When was your last holiday? ....

2 Where did you go? ....

3 Who did you go with? ....

4 What was the weather like? ....

5 What did you do? ....

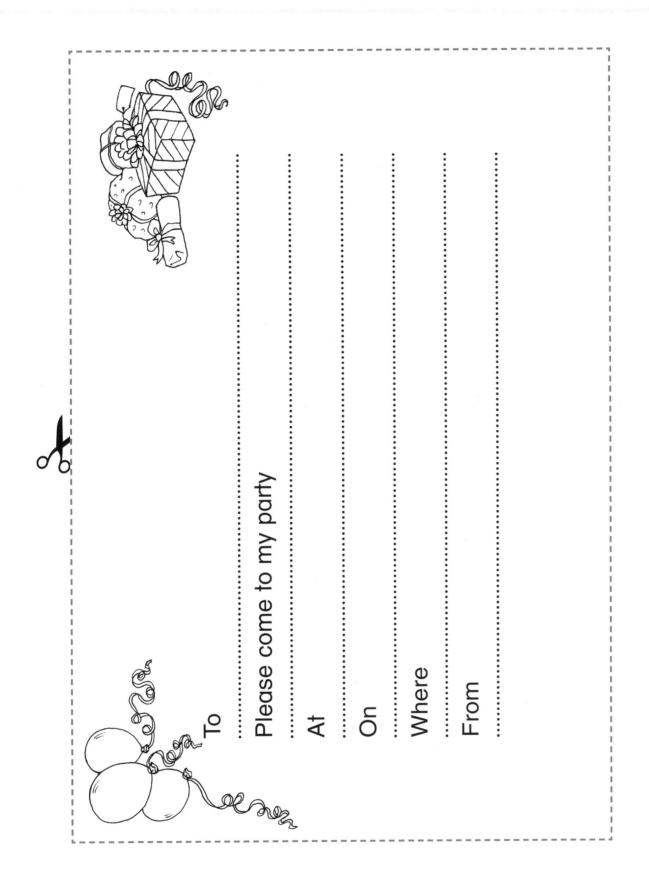

To ....

Please come to my party ....

At ....

On ....

Where ....

From ....

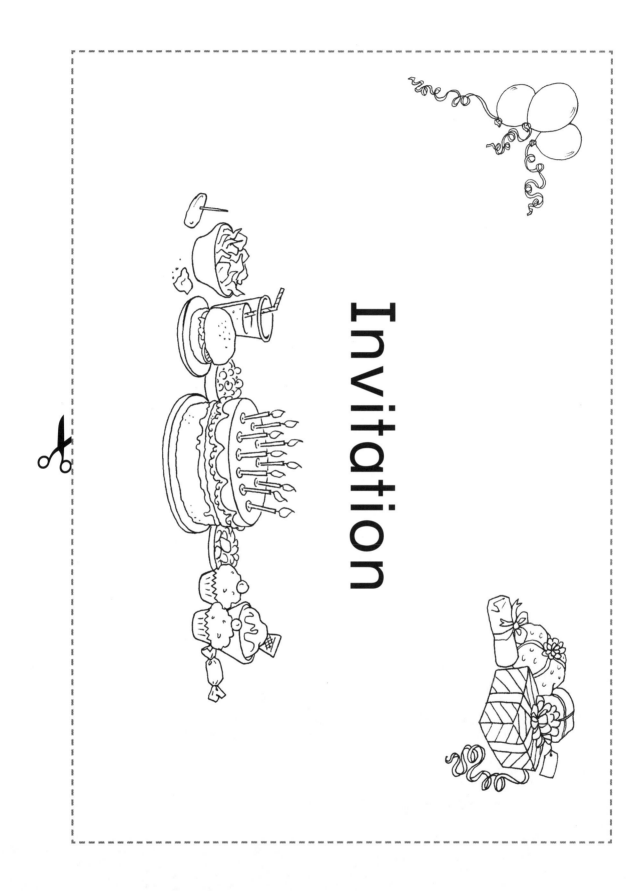

Invitation

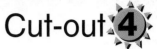

Sunday

Saturday

My diary

by

....

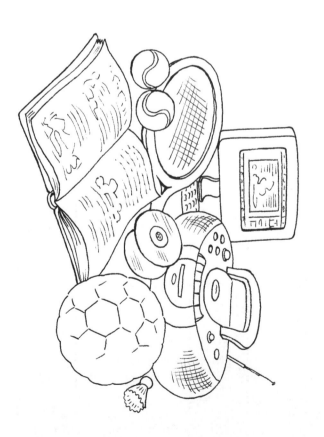

Monday	Tuesday	Wednesday	Thursday	Friday	Saturday	Sunday

I live in the ....

I live in a ....

It's got ....

....

I like living in the ....

because ....

....

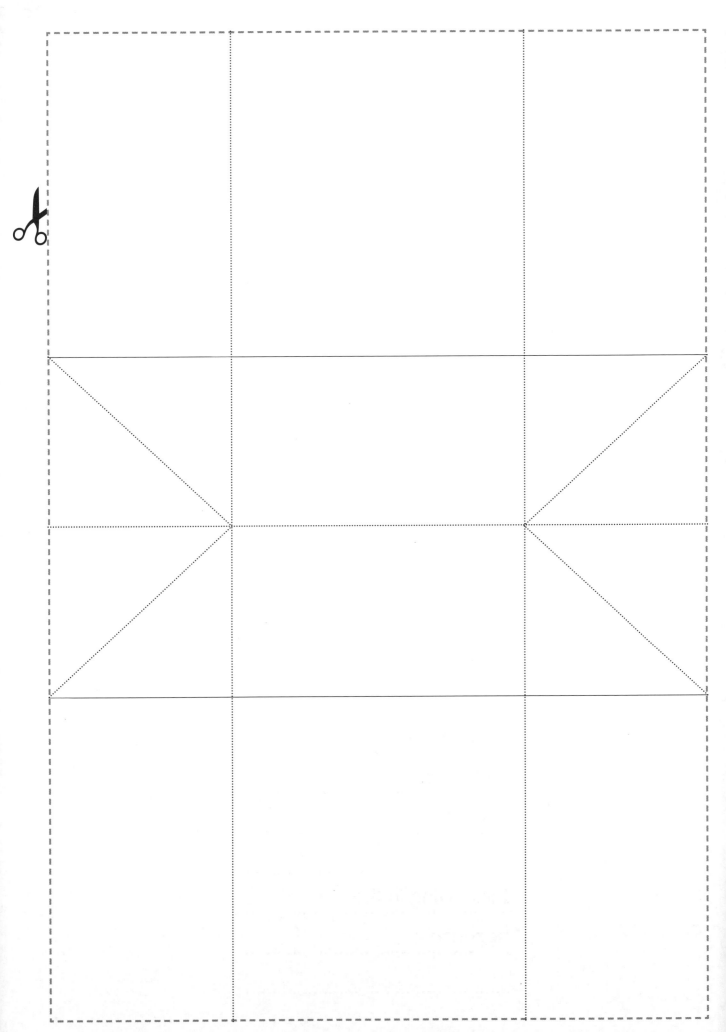

When I was young I

....   had/didn't have

....   wore/didn't wear

....   liked/didn't like

....   slept/didn't sleep

....   went/didn't go

....   could/couldn't

LESSON 8

① Read and write *yes* or *no*

> Look at the song in the Pupil's Book.

1 In verse 1, it's hot and sunny. ...yes...

2 In verse 2, it's wet and snowy. ....

3 In verse 3, it's cold and sunny. ....

4 The tall girl's wearing a hat and glasses. ....

5 The boy's carrying a football. ....

6 The small girl's wearing a scarf and gloves. ....

② Make a weather diary. Tell a friend. ➡ Cut-out 5

> On Monday it was sunny.

> On Thursday it was cold.

> Well done!

③ Tick what you can do. Colour the ladder.

I can spell weather words. ☐

I can say what the weather is/was like. ☐

I can talk about what I did on my holidays. ☐

I can write about my holidays. ☐

I can tell a story in the past tense. ☐

Very good

Good

OK

1 Read and write

can   hungry
biggest   clever
funny   ~~inside~~

Peter and Sally are at the zoo. They see some lions and a panda. The lions are **1** _inside_ their house. Sally likes the panda. It's **2** _____ . Peter can see a shark. He says it's the **3** _____ fish in the water. Then they see some dolphins. Dolphins are very **4** _____. Sally sees a parrot. The parrot is very **5** _____ . It **6** _____ talk.

2 Look at the pictures and write the words

1

_____lion_____

2

_____

3

_____

4
_____

3 Read and write the words

1 Elephants aren't weak, they're _____strong_____ .

2 A _____ is big and very strong. It's a type of cat.

3 In the zoo, some animals live in a _____ .

4 A _____ is black and white. It's a type of bear.

5 Sharks are the biggest _____ in the water.

LESSON 2

1 **Listen, colour and write** 🎧 16

2 **Look at the picture and write** *yes* **or** *no*

1   The lion is the biggest animal. ..*yes*....

2   The parrot is the smallest animal. ....

3   The parrot is green, red and blue. ....

4   The dolphins are bigger than the panda. ....

5   The dolphins are hungry. ....

3 **Read and write**

| whale | bat | monkey | shark |

1   It's grey and it's the biggest fish in the water. ....*shark*..........

2   It isn't a bird but it can fly. It's black. ....

3   It's brown. It climbs trees. It's the funniest animal. ....

4   It's very big. It can swim. It isn't a fish. ....

UNIT **6**

1 **Look at the picture in the Pupil's Book and complete the sentences**

1 The panda  *is dancing* .

2 The dolphins ....

3 The parrot ....

4 The kangaroo ....

5 The giraffe ....

2 **Listen and draw lines** 🎧 17

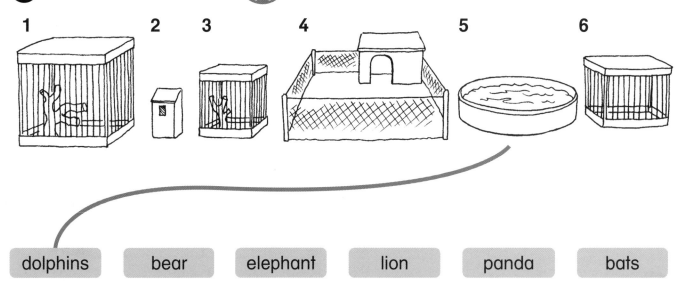

| dolphins | bear | elephant | lion | panda | bats |

3 **Read and choose the best answer**

1 Can you fly?   **a** No, I don't.   **b** Yes, I fly.   (**c** No, I can't.)

2 Can a kangaroo jump higher than a panda?
   a Yes, he can.   **b** Yes, it can.   **c** Yes, it does.

3 Are lions stronger than cats?
   a Yes, they can.   **b** Yes, they do.   **c** Yes, they are.

4 Can bats talk?   **a** No, can't.   **b** No, they can't.   **c** No, they don't.

5 Do dolphins eat fish?
   a Yes, they can.   **b** Yes, they do.   **c** Yes, dolphins are.

LESSON 4

UNIT 6

1 Listen and write 18

1 When: Saturday

2 How many kinds of animals:

3 Biggest animals:

4 Favourite animal:

5 Favourite animal's food:

2 Read and write the words

beautiful   ~~thirty~~
thirsty   best
cleverest

We went to the zoo on Saturday. We saw about

1 ....thirty.......... different animals. I liked the parrots

2 .... They were the most 3 ....

and the 4 .... They could talk and they

said, 'I'm hungry and I'm 5 .... !'

3 Find and write the words

1  kangaroo

2  ....

3  ....

4  ....

5  ....

6  ....

h	u	b	d	x	p	o	w
k	u	l	e	o	s	d	l
k	a	n	g	a	r	o	o
v	t	j	g	y	r	l	c
z	i	h	n	r	v	p	t
b	r	q	j	m	y	h	l
b	e	w	f	r	u	i	t
n	d	r	v	p	u	n	g

47

1 **Look at picture A in the Pupil's Book and write *yes* or *no***

Where's the lion?

1   The panda's next to the lion. ....*yes*....

2   The lion's inside its house. ....

3   The giraffe's eating some leaves. ....

4   The monkeys are sleeping. ....

5   The parrot's bigger than the panda. ....

2 **Look at pictures A and B. Write about the differences.**

1   .....*In picture A the lion's sleeping, in B it's awake.*.....................

2   ....

3   ....

4   ....

3 **Match the opposites**

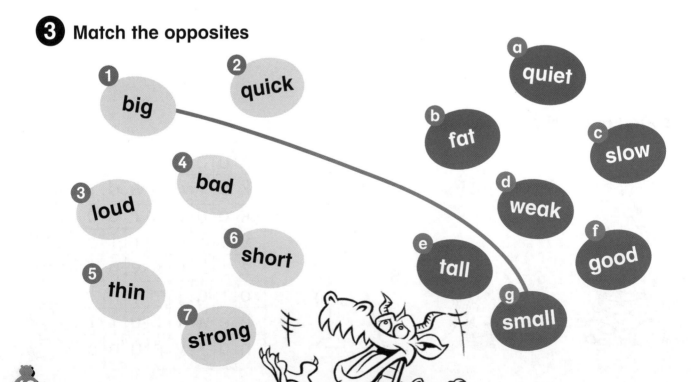

1 big

2 quick

3 loud

4 bad

5 thin

6 short

7 strong

a quiet

b fat

c slow

d weak

e tall

f good

g small

1 Read the story and write the words

parrot

monkeys

ice cream

dolphins

fish

friends

My name is John. I love all animals, but I like **1** *dolphins* best. For my last birthday party we went to the zoo. Five **2** .... came with me.

We saw the dolphins. The oldest dolphin was nine. The same age as me! It was their lunch time. They jumped out of the water and caught **3** .... that the zoo keeper threw for them. They were very hungry. One day I want to swim with dolphins.

Then we ate our lunch quickly and we went to see the **4** .... in their cage. I had an **5** .... in my hand and one clever monkey put his hand through the cage and took my ice cream!

Before we went home, we went to see the parrots and the zoo keeper said to me, 'This **6** .... wants to say something to you.' Do you know what the parrot did? It sang 'Happy birthday to you'! It sang really loudly! It was the cleverest parrot and the best birthday party!

2 Choose the correct words and write them on the lines

1 I like dolphins ......*best*...... .   **good   well   best**

2 They jumped out of the water and .... fish.   **catch caught catching**

3 We went to see the monkeys in .... cage.   **his   their   that**

4 This parrot wants .... something to you.   **say   saying   to say**

5 The parrot sang really ....   **loudly   louder   loud**

3 Draw a book cover and write the title

UNIT **6**

LESSON **7**

1 **Circle the odd one out and write**

1   *Bats aren't birds.*

2   ....

3   ....

4   ....

2 **Read and write**

1 Bats eat ....*fruit*........ and flies.

2 They're good at ....

3 They .... in the day.

4 They have .... wings.

5 They can't .... very well.

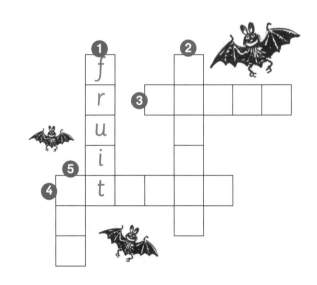

```
      1        2
      f
      r   3
      u
      i
  5   t
4
```

3 **Write the answers for you. Then ask a friend.**

1 Can you draw a dolphin? ....

2 Can you run faster than a lion? ....

3 Can you swim? ....

4 Do you like zoos? ....

5 What's your favourite animal? ....

50

1 **Read and write *yes* or *no*. Correct the 'no' sentences.**

1 Monkeys are stronger than lions.
No. Lions are stronger than monkeys.

2 The elephant is the biggest animal in the zoo.

....

3 The kangaroo is the smallest animal.

....

4 Giraffes are fatter than elephants.

....

5 A giraffe's legs are longer than a bear's legs.

....

2 **Make a zoo picture. Tell a friend.** ➡ **Cut-out 6**

My bear is strong. It's stronger than a kangaroo. It's the strongest animal.

Well done!

3 **Tick what you can do. Colour the ladder.**

I can say the names of zoo animals. ☐

I can describe and compare animals. ☐

I can match adjectives to their opposites. ☐

I can write about what animals can and can't do. ☐

I can tell a story. ☐

Very good

Good

OK

51

1 Read and write

upstairs ~~library~~
lift basement
thirsty floor

Peter and his grandmother are at the **1** _library_ .

Peter wants to look at dinosaur books. The dinosaur books

are **2** .... on the third **3** ....

Grandma goes upstairs in the **4** .... She sees

Peter. He's going downstairs to the **5** ....

Grandma finds Peter in the café. Peter went to the

basement because he was **6** ....

2 Look at the pictures and write the words

1   2   3   4

bank   ....

3 Read and write the words

1   You can walk upstairs or you can take the _lift_ .

2   You go .... to get from the top floor to the basement.

3   You need a drink when you feel ....

4   You go to the library to look at ....

5   You can drink .... out of a cup.

LESSON 2

1 Listen, colour and write 19

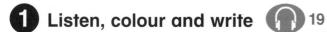

2 Look at the picture and write *yes* or *no*

1   The bus is at the bus station. ....yes....

2   The bus driver is driving the bus. ....

3   The man is downstairs on the bus. ....

4   The bus driver is eating a sandwich. ....

5   The woman is downstairs on the bus. ....

3 Read and write

parents   **grandson**   **grown up**   **granddaughter**

1   This is your son/daughter's son. ......*grandson*......

2   This is your son/daughter's daughter. ....

3   These are your mum and dad. ....

4   This is an adult not a child. ....

1 **Look at the picture in the Pupil's Book and complete the sentences**

1 There are three people _outside the cafe_ .

2 The grandparents are with their ....

3 The little girl is drinking ....

4 There are five people ....

5 The bank has got ....

2 **Listen and draw lines** 🎧 20

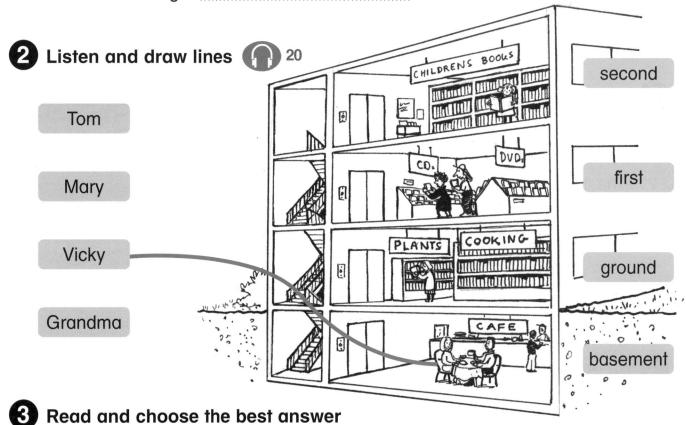

Tom

Mary

Vicky

Grandma

second

first

ground

basement

3 **Read and choose the best answer**

1 Excuse me. Where's the cinema?
a It's opposite the bank **b** Yes, there is. **c** You go there to see films.

2 Is it next to the hospital?
a No, they aren't. **b** No, it isn't. **c** No, it doesn't.

3 What's she drinking?
a She drinks milk. **b** Yes, she's drinking. **c** She's drinking milk.

4 Do you think there's a lift?
a Yes, I think. **b** Yes, I do. **c** Yes, I am.

LESSON **4**

1 **Listen and write** 🎧 21

1 Name: _Emily_

2 When:

3 How many places:

4 Drink:

5 Bought:

2 **Read and write the words**

film
toothbrush
~~swimming pool~~
soup   salad

Yesterday I went to the **1** _swimming pool_ in the morning, then I went shopping. I bought a CD and then I went to the supermarket to buy a new **2** ....

I had lunch in the café. I had a bowl of

3 .... and some **4** ....

Then I went to the cinema to see a **5** ....

3 **Find and write the words**

1

bank

4

....

2

....

5

....

3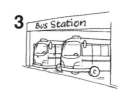

....

6

....

k	b	t	l	f	r	z	s	o	i
d	s	a	i	h	j	b	a	n	k
g	q	c	b	w	m	a	n	u	y
b	m	e	r	t	f	s	d	x	e
v	c	a	a	n	w	e	w	l	b
b	w	y	r	a	j	m	i	o	p
x	d	f	y	k	l	e	c	a	b
h	y	e	o	m	e	n	h	j	z
b	u	s	s	t	a	t	i	o	n

1 **Look at picture A in the Pupil's Book and write *yes* or *no***

1   They're at the supermarket. .....*yes*.....

2   There are four children in the picture. ....

3   The girl's eating an apple. ....

4   Mum's buying orange juice. ....

5   There's coffee in the trolley. ....

2 **Look at pictures A and B. Write about the differences.**

1   *In picture A there's a boy sitting in the trolley, in B there's a girl.*

2   ....

3   ....

4   ....

3 **Look at the pictures and the letters. Write the words.**

1  _cheese_   h e e / e s c

4  _ _ _ _ _ _   p t s / a a s

2  _ _ _ _ _ _   e e f / f o c

5  _ _ _ _   p u s o

3  _ _ _ _ _   i r / t u f

6  _ _ _   a t e

LESSON 6

1 Read the story and write the words

scarf

music

bottle

pineapple

CD

toothbrush

Last weekend, Jenny went to town to buy a toothbrush. In the big supermarket she heard her favourite **1** _music_ and so she looked for the **2** _____ . Opposite the CDs there were some clothes. She wanted a new T-shirt and she found a nice red one. Then she thought, 'It's Mum's birthday tomorrow' and she looked for a birthday present. She bought a nice **3** _____ . Then she was hungry and she bought a sandwich and a **4** _____ of juice. Next to the juice, there was lots of fruit. She loves fruit so she bought some apples, some pears and a **5** _____ . Before she went home, she also bought a book to read on the bus.

On the bus she looked in her bags. Oh, no! She didn't buy a **6** _____ !

2 Choose the correct words and write them on the lines

1   Jenny went to town ___to___ buy a toothbrush.   **to   at   so**

2   Opposite the CDs there _____ some clothes.   **was   were   are**

3   She looked _____ a birthday present.   **to   in   for**

4   She bought a bottle _____ juice.   **for   of   with**

5   She bought a book to _____ on the bus home.   **reading   see   read**

3 Draw a book cover and write the title

UNIT **7**

LESSON **7**

1 Circle the odd one out and write

1 A bear isn't a place in a town. ....

2 ....

....

3 ....

....

4 ....

....

2 Read and write

1 You can buy _everything_ at big supermarkets.

2 Your .... went to many different shops.

3 Most .... have one or two supermarkets.

4 You can have .... in the café.

5 They .... meat from one shop.

```
              ①
              e
              v
              e         ③
②g r _ _ _ _ _ _ _ 
              y         _
              t    ④    
              h  ⑤_ _ _ _ 
              i
              n
              g
```

3 Write the answers for you. Then ask a friend.

1 How many supermarkets are there in your town? ....

2 Do you sometimes go to the supermarket? ....

3 Do you go by bus? ....

4 Do you like going to the supermarket? ....

5 What are/were your grandparent's names? ....

58

LESSON 8

1 Read and write *yes* or *no*. Correct the 'no' sentences.

1   You catch a bus at the cinema.
      No. You catch a bus at the bus station.

2   You go to the library to read books.

      ....

3   You buy food at the supermarket.

      ....

4   You play inside at the park.

      ....

5   You go to the bank when you aren't well.

      ....

When's the
next bus?

CINEMA

NOW
SHOWING

2 Make a wordsearch. Give it to a friend.

➡ Cut-out 7

Well done!

3 Tick what you can do. Colour the ladder.

I can name places in a town. ☐

I can write about different floors in a building. ☐

I can talk about what we do in town. ☐

I can describe my family. ☐

I can say what we buy in supermarkets. ☐

Very
good

Good

OK

UNIT 8 The world around us

LESSON 1

1 Read and write

cow countryside
quieter fields
climbing river

Jane lives in the **1** countryside . She lives on a farm.
Her house is near a **2** _____ . She likes the
countryside. She says it is **3** _____ than the
town. There are lots of **4** _____ and trees. Daisy
says she isn't good at **5** _____ trees. They see a
6 _____ . Daisy climbs a tree very quickly!

2 Look at the pictures and write the words

1

...... rabbit ......

2

....

3

....

4

....

3 Read and write the words

1 A ...... river ...... starts in the mountains and ends in the sea.

2 Cows eat _____ in fields.

3 The _____ is quieter than the town.

4 A lake is bigger than a swimming pool, but _____ than the sea.

5 A rabbit is _____ than a bird.

60

LESSON 2

1 **Listen, colour and write** 🎧 22

2 **Look at the picture and write *yes* or *no***

1 The children are in a town. ....no....

2 The girl's sitting on a yellow and green blanket. ....

3 They're having a picnic near a lake. ....

4 There are two rabbits in the picture. ....

5 You can fish in the river. ....

3 **Read and write**

| picnic | farmer | rabbit | village |

1 This place is smaller than a city and a town. ....*village*.......

2 You have this when you sit on a blanket and eat outside. ....

3 This animal has a round tail and can run and jump. ....

4 This person lives in the country and works on a farm. ....

UNIT 8

LESSON 3

1 **Look at the picture in the Pupil's Book and complete the sentences**

1 There are about twelve *houses in the village* .

2 The farm is in a field ....

3 There are lots of trees in the ....

4 Behind the forest there are ....

5 There are about five cars on ....

2 **Listen and draw lines** 23

1 ((o))   2   3   4   5 ((o))

| Friday | Saturday | Sunday | Monday | Tuesday |

3 **Read and choose the best answer**

1 Can you see a city?   **a** No, I can't.   **b** No, I don't.   **c** No, it isn't.

2 Is there a farm near here?   **a** Yes, there's.   **b** Yes, it is.   **c** Yes, there is.

3 Would you like to live in the country?
   a Yes, I do.   **b** Yes, I like it.   **c** Yes, I would.

4 Where's the farm?
   a It's a place where farmers work.   **b** It's near the river.   **c** Yes, it does.

62

LESSON 4

1 Listen and write 🎧 24

1 Home: *the city*

2 First place: _____

3 Picnic food: _____

4 Animals: _____

5 Favourite place: _____

2 Read and write the words

| lake   riding |
| waterfall |
| tired   climbed |
| ~~holiday~~ |

We had a good **1** *holiday* in the countryside.

We went **2** _____ in the forest on Monday. On

Tuesday we walked to a **3** _____ . On Thursday

we **4** _____ a mountain. On Friday, we went sailing

on a **5** _____ . I'm very **6** _____ now!

3 Find and write the words

1
surprised

2
....

3
....

4
....

5
....

6
....

w	j	s	a	i	l	i	n	g	s
w	n	p	g	s	q	v	f	y	u
d	a	n	v	z	l	u	o	t	r
b	y	t	k	s	r	o	r	m	p
v	c	j	e	w	b	x	e	k	r
f	s	a	p	r	b	g	s	l	i
b	v	m	d	s	f	j	t	q	s
z	m	o	u	n	t	a	i	n	e
g	y	o	e	c	h	u	l	k	d
p	o	n	c	f	l	z	d	l	o

1 **Look at picture A in the Pupil's Book and write *yes* or *no***

There's a bird above my head.

1   There's a busy road below the mountains.   *no*

2   The sun is above the mountains. ....

3   It's a cloudy and rainy day. ....

4   There are a lot of cars on the road. ....

5   There's a big lake near the village. ....

2 **Look at pictures A and B. Write about the differences.**

1   *In picture A the sun's above the mountains, in B it's the moon.*

2   ....

3   ....

4   ....

3 **Match the words**

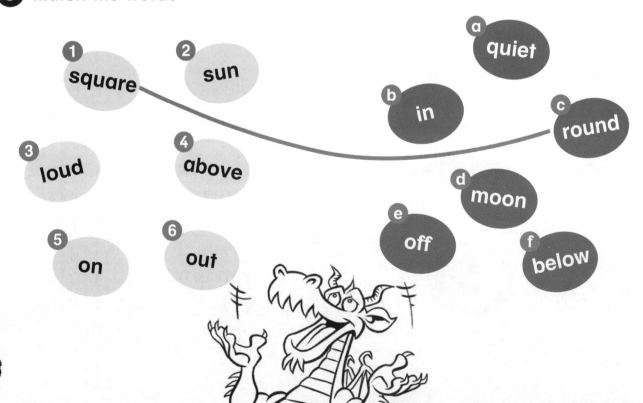

LESSON 6

1 **Read the story and write the words**

bus

handbag

flat

house

photos

balcony

Our cousins are staying with us this week. They live in a

1 .....house..... in the countryside and we live in a

2 .... in the city. They like the city, but they think it

is very busy and there are lots of cars. They like our small

flat and they love going in the lift. They think our

3 .... is very small because they have a big

garden at their house.

Yesterday they took a **4** .... for the first time. They

sat upstairs and took lots of photos of famous places. Then

we went to a café for lunch and to the cinema. When we got

home, we looked at the photos. There were twelve good

5 .... and thirty-five of the inside of Aunt Mary's

6 .... ! They want to go on the bus again to take

more photos!

2 **Choose the correct words and write them on the lines**

1 Our cousins live ......*in*........ the countryside.   **in on at**

2 They love .... in the lift.   **go goes going**

3 They think our balcony is small ....
   they have a big garden.   **because so but**

4 Yesterday they .... a bus for the first time.   **taking take took**

5 They want .... on the bus again.   **to go going gone**

3 **Draw a book cover and write the title**

65

UNIT **8**

LESSON **7**

1 **Circle the odd one out and write**

1   *A supermarket isn't in the countryside.*

2

3

4

2 **Read and write**

1   You can ......sleep...... on some trains.

2   Trains can go to some .... where cars can't go.

3   The .... way to see the world is by train.

4   Trains can go into .... and forests where there aren't any roads.

5   You don't get tired because you don't .... a train.

| **1** s | l | e | e | p |

3 **Write the answers for you. Then ask a friend.**

1   Do you sometimes go to the countryside? ....

2   Do you live near mountains or a forest? ....

3   Do you sometimes travel by train? ....

4   Do you like going in a train? ....

5   Are there any famous places near where you live? ....

1 **Read and write *yes* or *no*. Correct the 'no' sentences.**

1 Bikes are faster than trains.
   No. Trains are faster than bikes.

2 There are sometimes waterfalls in the mountains.
   ....

3 The countryside is quieter than the city.
   ....

4 Lots of people live in flats in the countryside.
   ....

5 Farms are usually in the city.
   ....

2 **Make a house. Tell a friend.** ➡ **Cut-out 8**

I live in the town. I live in a flat. It's got a balcony. I like living in the town because it's busy.

Well done!

3 **Tick what you can do. Colour the ladder.**

I can name things that you see in the countryside. ☐

I can spell countryside words. ☐

I can compare the town and the countryside. ☐

I can write about what you can do in the countryside. ☐

I can talk about my favourite place. ☐

Very good

Good

OK

In the playground

1 Read and write

behind   loudly
counting
sleeping
children

The **1** *children* are playing in the playground. Mary and Jack are **2** .... to a hundred. The other children are hiding. Jane's hiding in a tree. Peter and Paul are hiding **3** .... the bikes. Mary finds Jill because Jill is laughing **4** .... They can't find Sally. Then Mary finds Sally. She's **5** .... !

2 Look at the pictures and write the words

1

hiding

2

....

3

....

4

....

3 Read and write the words

1 We ..... *play* ..... in the playground at lunch time.

2 Can you .... to a hundred in English?

3 Peter is .... behind the bikes.

4 Jill is .... behind Mary.

5 They .... to go back to the classroom.

One, two, three...

LESSON **2**

1 Listen, colour and write 🎧 25

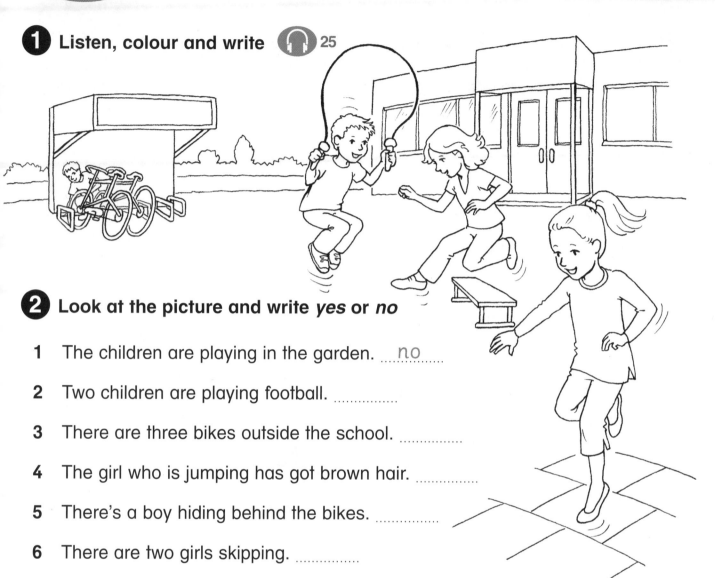

2 Look at the picture and write *yes* or *no*

1 The children are playing in the garden. ....no....

2 Two children are playing football. ....

3 There are three bikes outside the school. ....

4 The girl who is jumping has got brown hair. ....

5 There's a boy hiding behind the bikes. ....

6 There are two girls skipping. ....

3 Read and write

hopping   **dancing**   **ninety-nine**   **skipping**

1 This is jumping with a rope. ......skipping......

2 The number before a hundred is ....

3 You can do this to music. ....

4 You do this on one leg. ....

UNIT 9

LESSON 3

1 **Look at the picture in the Pupil's Book and complete the sentences**

1 Five children are eating _..their lunch.........._ .

2 The boy under the tree is .... and ....

3 One boy and two girls ....

4 One girl's reading ....

5 One boy's carrying ....

2 **Listen and draw lines** 🎧 26

1   2   3   4   5   6

Ann   May   Fred   Nick   Lucy   Ted

3 **Read and choose the best answer**

1 What are you doing?   **a** I run.   **b** I'm running.   **c** I do.

2 Are you good at sport?   **a** Yes, it's good.   **b** Yes, I do.   **c** Yes, I am.

3 What are they doing?   **a** They play.   **b** They're playing.   **c** Yes, they are.

4 Is he hiding?   **a** No, he doesn't.   **b** He doesn't hide.   **c** No, he isn't.

5 What's he carrying?   **a** It's a camera.   **b** He's got one.   **c** Playing baseball.

LESSON 4

1 Listen and write 🎧 27

1 When: Saturday morning

2 What activity: _____

3 How many children: _____

4 What kind of food: _____

5 Whose party: _____

2 Read and write the words

~~party~~
sleeping
taking
skating   came

These are photos of my birthday **1** ___party___ . In this one we're **2** _____ the bus into town. This is me and Jill. We're **3** _____ . We **4** _____ home on the bus. This is a photo of Mary. She's **5** _____ .

3 Find and write the words

1    2    3

skating   ....

4    5    6

v	d	s	k	a	t	i	n	g	k
e	n	k	u	p	d	b	x	y	w
a	z	y	i	q	n	h	f	s	r
t	l	o	r	c	b	h	t	c	u
i	o	c	d	g	k	f	a	i	n
n	f	w	a	s	h	i	n	g	n
g	r	h	m	p	s	l	n	t	i
j	r	l	o	o	k	i	n	g	n
o	n	c	f	l	z	d	l	o	g

....

1 **Look at picture A in the Pupil's Book and write *yes* or *no***

I always cry at sad films.

1 The baby in the pram is crying. ....*yes*....

2 The brown dog is sleeping under a tree. ....

3 There's a man who is throwing a ball. ....

4 The woman with the baby is sitting down. ....

5 There are two girls running and jumping. ....

2 **Look at pictures A and B. Write about the differences.**

1 *In picture A the dog's running, but in B it's dreaming.*..............

2 ....

3 ....

4 ....

3 **Look at the pictures and the letters. Write the words.**

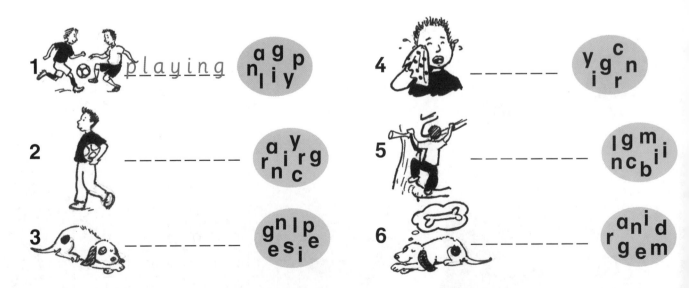

1 <u>playing</u>   a g p n l i y

2 _ _ _ _ _ _   a y r i r g n c

3 _ _ _ _ _ _   g n l p e s i e

4 _ _ _ _ _ _   y c g n i r

5 _ _ _ _ _ _   l g m n c b i i

6 _ _ _ _ _ _   a n i d r g e m

LESSON **6**

UNIT **9**

1 Read the story and write the words

doctor

first

foot

running

walk

sunny

skipping

My name's Jack. We had sports day at school last week. It

was a nice **1** ....*sunny*.......... day. The first race was

2 .... which is my favourite. My friend Paul is better

at running than me and Peter is the best. Peter was

3 .... , Paul was second and I was third. Jane

came last. She doesn't like running, but she loves

4 .... She skips more quickly than everyone else

but on sports day she hurt her **5** ....

Our teacher, Miss Green, ran to her and asked, 'What's the

matter?' and Jane said, 'I can't **6** .... '. Miss Green

and another teacher carried her inside. My dad is a

7 .... He took off Jane's shoes and socks and

looked at her foot. It hurt but it was OK. Jane couldn't do any

more sports that day, but she watched us and took photos.

2 Choose the correct words and write them on the lines

1   I ......*like*...... running best.   **like   likes   liking**

2   I came .... in the race.   **three   third   thirteen**

3   Jane doesn't like ....   **run   runs   running**

4   On sports day she hurt .... foot.   **his   her   hers**

5   Miss Green and another
     teacher .... her inside.   **carrying   carries   carried**

3 Draw a book cover and write the title

73

1 Circle the odd one out and write

1 .....A playground isn't a sport.....

2 ....

3 ....

4 ....

2 Read and write

1 You must always skate ...carefully... .

2 When you are better, you can go ....

3 You wear .... on your feet.

4 Skating is exciting, it's never ....

5 At first you must skate ....

Crossword: 1 c / a / r / e / f / u / l / l / y

3 Write the answers for you. Then ask a friend.

1 Do you sometimes go skating? ....

2 Do you like skating? ....

3 Which sports do you like? ....

4 When is your sports day? ....

5 Do you sometimes dream when you're sleeping? ....

74

1 **Read and write *yes* or *no*. Correct the 'no' sentences.**

1 You wear shoes when you go skating.
   No. You wear skates. ....

2 Skating is easy.
   ....

3 You dream when you're sleeping.
   ....

4 Walking is faster than running.
   ....

5 'B' is the second letter of the alphabet.
   ....

2 **Make a *Guess who* game. Play with a friend.** ➡ **Cut-out 9**

Is he crying?

No, he isn't.

Well done!

3 **Tick what you can do. Colour the ladder.**

I can talk about playground activities. ☐

I can write about what people are doing. ☐

I can talk about skating. ☐

I can count up to a hundred. ☐

I can tell a story. ☐

Very
good

Good

OK

10 Then and now

1 Read and write

didn't   films
grandmother
DVDs   read

Daisy is talking to her **1** grandmother. Her

grandmother is telling her about when she was young.

She had a TV but she **2** .... have a

computer. They watched **3** .... in black and

white. They didn't have **4** .... They had to

go to the cinema to see films. In the evening, they

5 .... books, talked and went to bed.

2 Look at the pictures and write the words

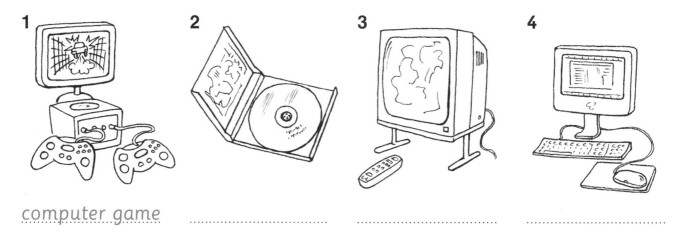

1   2   3   4

computer game   ....

3 Read and write the words

1   Daisy's grandmother loves computer   games   .

2   You can go to the .... to see films.

3   When Grandma .... young, there weren't any computers.

4   They watched TV in .... and white.

5   In the evening, they talked and they .... to bed.

LESSON 2

1 **Listen, colour and write** 🎧 28

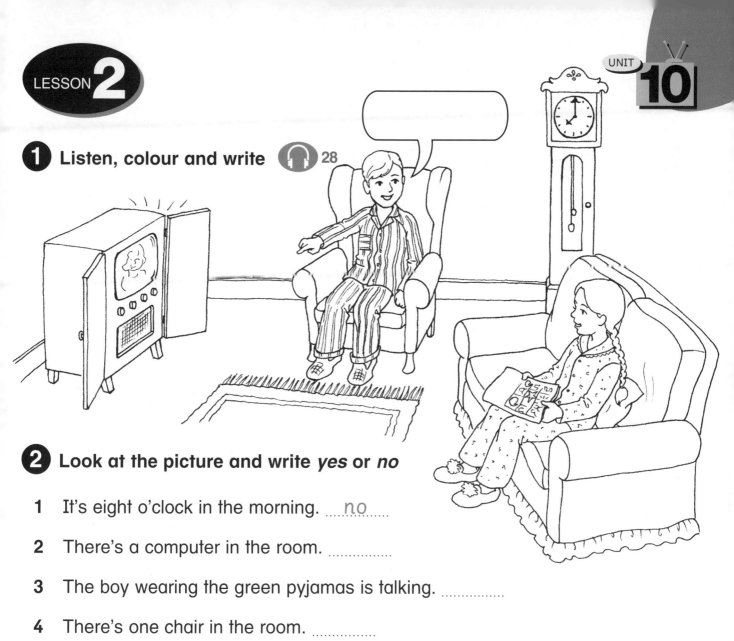

2 **Look at the picture and write *yes* or *no***

1   It's eight o'clock in the morning. ....no....

2   There's a computer in the room. ....

3   The boy wearing the green pyjamas is talking. ....

4   There's one chair in the room. ....

5   The girl with the pink pyjamas is reading a book. ....

3 **Read and write**

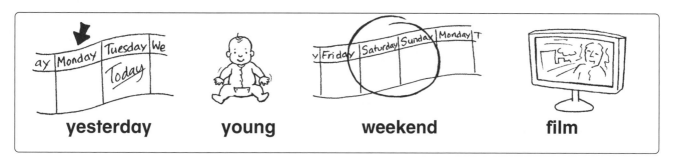

yesterday   **young**   **weekend**   **film**

1   These are the two days at the end of the week. ....weekend........

2   This is the opposite of old. ....

3   This is something you watch on TV or at the cinema. ....

4   This is the day before today. ....

1 **Look at the picture in the Pupil's Book and complete the sentences**

1   This is an old picture of *a town*   .

2   There are five ....

3   There isn't a ....

4   Next to the cinema there's a ....

5   Some people are wearing ....

2 **Listen and draw lines** 🎧 29

| four | six | eight | nine | ten | eleven |

3 **Read and choose the best answer**

1   Did you have a TV when you were young?
   a Yes, we did.   **b** Yes, we had.   **c** Yes, it was.

2   How old were you in this photo?   **a** I'm nine.   **b** I were nine.   **c** I was nine.

3   What did you wear?   **a** I wear a hat.   **b** I wore a hat.   **c** I'm wearing a hat.

4   Did you watch DVDs?   **a** No, we don't.   **b** No, we weren't.   **c** No, we didn't.

5   Were there supermarkets in the past?
   a No, there weren't.   **b** Yes, it is.   **c** No, there aren't.

 **LESSON 4**

1 **Listen and write** 🎧 30

1 Who: *grandparents*

2 Lived:

3 Could buy:

4 Worked:

5 Liked doing:

2 **Read and write the words**

~~could~~   bike
badminton
started   fifth

She 1 .....*could*..... walk when she was one and she

could ride a 2 .... when she was two. She got

a new bike on her 3 .... birthday. She

4 .... to play tennis when she was six or

seven. Now she likes playing 5 ....

3 **Find and write the words**

1

tennis

2

....

3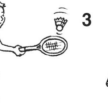

....

4

....

5

....

6

....

n	g	s	w	n	p	g	o	q	m
f	y	u	d	a	n	v	n	l	u
o	t	z	b	v	j	e	a	n	s
t	k	e	r	o	i	m	p	v	i
q	e	w	n	b	x	d	k	r	c
p	r	b	g	n	s	l	e	i	b
v	b	a	d	m	i	n	t	o	n
m	d	s	f	j	t	s	q	v	s
v	e	g	e	t	a	b	l	e	s
e	c	h	l	k	d	p	o	d	l

1 **Look at picture A in the Pupil's Book and write *yes* or *no***

1 The children who are sitting on the armchairs are watching TV. ___no___

2 The boy's playing a computer game on the computer. _____

3 There are three armchairs in the living room. _____

4 The woman's wearing a long coat and a hat. _____

5 The man's writing a letter with a pen. _____

2 **Look at pictures A and B. Write about the differences.**

1 *In picture A the man's writing a letter, in B he's sending an email.*

2 ....

3 ....

4 ....

3 **Match the words**

1 watched
2 listened to
3 read
4 wrote
5 played
6 wore

a CDs
b jeans
c emails
d videos
e comic
f computer games

1 Read the story and write the words

laughed

cried

one

blanket

upstairs

bedroom

cupboard

When we were small, my younger brother and I slept in

1 ....*one*.... bedroom. He had a blue **2** .... on

his bed and I had a yellow one on mine. We had a lot of toys

and books and our clothes were in a small **3** ....

We had to go to bed early, but when Mum and Dad went

downstairs, we got up again and played quietly for a long time.

One night we **4** .... very loudly and Mum came

5 .... We hid under our blankets, but she could

hear us. Mum knew we were awake, but she went back

downstairs.

The next day, I had to sleep in a different room. I was happy

because I was the older sister and I didn't want to be in a room

with my younger brother. My brother **6** .... when I

moved. He was afraid and he couldn't sleep. Now, he's happy in

his **7** .... and I'm happy in mine. We have our yellow

and blue blankets on our beds, but they're very small now.

2 Choose the correct words and write them on the lines

1   We ....*slept*.... in one bedroom.   **slept   sleeping   asleep**

2   Our clothes .... in a small cupboard.   **was   were   is**

3   We played .... for a long time.   **quiet   quieter   quietly**

4   Mum knew we were ....   **waking up   awake   awoke**

5   My brother .... when I moved.   **cried   cries   crying**

3 Draw a book cover and write the title

UNIT 10

① Circle the odd one out and write

1   *You wear a coat and jeans,*
      but you watch a TV.

2   ....

      ....

3   ....

      ....

4   ....

      ....

② Read and write

1   People can sit in their armchairs
    and buy things.

2   Many people have .... at home.

3   Before, people had to write with a
    pen and ....

4   Now they can write .... very quickly.

5   People found .... to their
    questions from books.

Crossword (down): a r m c h a i r s

③ Write the answers for you. Then ask a friend.

1   Have you got a computer at home? ....

2   What do you use your computer for? ....

3   Do you write emails? ....

4   Do you ever go to the library? ....

5   Do you think computers are good for us? ....

LESSON 8

1 **Read and write *yes* or *no*. Correct the 'no' sentences.**

1 Our grandparents didn't have computers.
   Yes.
   ....

2 They wrote emails.
   ....

3 They wore jeans when they were young.
   ....

4 They had black and white TVs.
   ....

5 They had fast cars.
   ....

2 **Make a picture of the past. Tell a friend.** ➡ Cut-out 10

When I was young, I wore shorts and I couldn't ride a bike.

Well done!

3 **Tick what you can do. Colour the ladder.**

I can spell the names of shops. ☐

I can talk about the past. ☐

I can write about my grandparents. ☐

I can talk about when I was young. ☐

I can tell a story. ☐

Very good

Good

OK